to: _____

from: _____

date: _____

In Honor of Your Great Journey

The Race

Hasan Davis, J.D.

justUS
BOOKS

an imprint of Martin Sisters Publishing

Published by JustUs Books,
an imprint of
Martin Sisters Publishing Company, Inc.
www. martinsisterspublishing.com
Copyright © 2019 Hasan Davis

Published in the United States
by Martin Sisters Publishing Company, Inc.

ISBN: 978-1-62553-983-0
Poetry
Creative Advocacy

Printed in the United States of America

DEDICATION

This book is dedicated to the hope dealers who insisted and persisted in helping young minds escape the many versions of Room 8. Thank you for your encouragement and your patience. Thank you for being able to hold a double vision for us; to clearly see the challenges we were experiencing in the moment while still being able to imagine with us an amazing version of us as champions.

This book is dedicated to the courageous minds young and old who are not willing to wait in a box for someone to give you permission to be your most amazing version of yourself, don't stop looking for the window... it is right there!

ACKNOWLEDGEMENTS

I would like to acknowledge,

My amazing wife Dreama who was able to see a dim flicker of light and imagine the inferno it could unleash.

My mother Alice Lovelace for being my first Inspiration and Hope Dealer, for giving me the gift of words that would ultimately unlock the prison of my mind.

My dad Charles Jikki Riley for helping me understand that I get to choose who and what I am to the world, and I get to own all that comes with that choice.

Dr. Lorraine Wilson who told me that I could do anything and dared me not to make her appear a fool for believing such a thing.

My father Alfreddie Charles Davis for giving me the opportunity to learn how liberating forgiveness can be.

My siblings by blood or shared sacrifice for dancing with me through a world of chaos and wonder, clueless that we were not supposed to dream of greatness together.

The literal masses of friends and family, who managed to show patience, grace, restraint, curiosity, and love even when I clearly did not deserve these gifts.

PROLOGUE

For most of my early childhood my experience of education was teachers trying to convince me that I belonged someplace special. Whether it was the hallway, the coat room, the detention room, or the corner they would say, "This is where kids like you belong."

I am blessed to have had remarkable people in my life who flipped the deficit model on its head. Instead of counting all the ways I was broken, they saw the gifts and the assets of a differently thinking, differently able child. That was a game changer. In time, I began to believe that I had a right to be in any class at any level, even in places I had never dared to go. I was no longer willing to tell myself that I wasn't good enough.

This book is a testament to the courageous who refuse to give up on their dreams and the fierce Hope Dealers who constantly remind them where the open window might be that leads to their next race.

It was a day like
the rest,
me sitting right there

With the lost kids,
in another special class
where

We would fit the round pegs

into square holes all day

As the teachers excuse we were

made just this way.

There's no need to be worried,
and no reason for stress

Your poor lives are not fair,
so you should just do your best.

These last words they'd sing as
they settled us all down,

Passing glue and round scissors
for our Popsicle stick crowns.

While crafting a band

for my Popsicle crown,

I reached hand into pocket

and guess what I found?

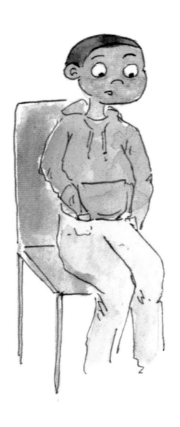

It was a note from my mother,
again like last week.

A reminder, things don't have
to stay as we see.

Written big in bold letters,

more easily read ...

It still took me a while,

but here's

what the note said:

I will love you, each day, like the first you were mine,

But to change in their eyes you must first change your mind!

If you want new results you can't accept what they say
About your "needs" that make them think this box is OK.

To put an eagle with chicks does not mean it's to blame,

But one day must still fly or will fail

just the same.

So, keep your mind on your dreams,

And your eyes on that door,

The inevitable victory can still be yours.

To raise you up high, any risk I would

take,

But you my dear child, you must plan

this escape!

Not having a clue what that

last line inferred,

I returned to my crown without

much of a word.

The next minute there
I spent disbelieving.

No way could my eyes see what
they were perceiving.

A window just appeared,

where there had been none before,

Among these walls, and locks,

and peep holes and door.

From where this thing came
I could hardly have guessed,

But warm light and cool breeze
had soon captured my breath.

And outside the window
I heard sounds unknown,

Sounds of cheering and laughter
and loud microphones.

There were announcers announcing,

on their loudspeakers speaking,

Welcoming all the champions
from that race on last weekend.

They said, "Today is today
and last week was back then,

On a day like this, folks,
anyone could still win!"

Looking back, I now realize
they did not expect me,

To take those words
and excitement so personally.

But there's no control over
words that we say,

Once out of the mouth
we translate our own way.

Every ear that can hear
must interpret for self,

So, I picked up my note
and started to climb that shelf.

I quick slipped past the teachers

and over the pane

Of that window before they could

close it again.

Then I shimmied down columns

just right for escaping,

And ran hard to the place

where those people were pacing.

I arrived at this field,

was amazed by the scene,

Of these runners and jumpers

from all types of teams.

They were stretching and reaching,

after training for months,

To take the first challenge,

to clear the high jump.

And like antelope they leaped,

none knew fear or seemed hopeless,

So, I slipped into line, praying

no one would notice.

But someone did see through

my thin veiled disguise,

It might have been the boots,

or the scared look in my eyes.

I asked, "please can I try this?
it looks like a blast!

Not like making those crowns
from old Popsicle stick trash."

As judges hemmed
and then hawed,
they explained the plain truth,

"Your training, your skills,
are not for this pursuit."

They removed me from line
as the stars started starting,

when from up in the bleachers
big voices began barking.

"Maybe he's lightning,
just been bottled too long."

"You might think he's weak
but what if he is strong?"

"Nobody has ever tried
hard as he'd try."

"And, even if he falls down,
he most likely won't die!"

From what I can guess

were new fans of mine,

And my mother,

who must have been there

the whole time,

Came demands I be given
one shot at that bar,

Despite having no chance
to show talent thus far.

So, they made me some room
and then let me back in,

Quite sure there was no way
I could actually win.

But soon the time came
I was finally on,

At the line with silence
so deafeningly long.

In good humor they played,
started lowering the bar,

for this unknown, untested
not right superstar.

But I whistled and waved,
"Hey, you raise that right back,

I can't break your records
with a low jump like that!"

So, rolling their eyes

and with fiendish sly grins,

they quick raised my bar

all the way up to 10!

As they smiled and high-fived

I heard one of them say,

"Do you think that boy's

smart enough to just walk away?"

But they all seemed surprised
as in hiking boot clumping,

I charged toward the mark
they had set for my jumping.

And with vision so clear
I could hardly see through it,

I leaped for that bar
as if nothing was to it.

There I floated, no, SAILED,
as the whole crowd
stopped breathing,

Watching me attempt this,
they were not quite believing.

Now, I didn't quite make it over.
More truthful to say.

See, I barely made HALF
of the distance that day.

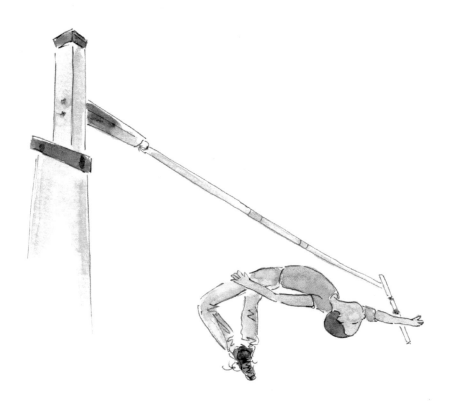

No sooner flat on the mat
I was pumping my fist,

Reminding the crowd,
I was quite new to this.

But what they could not have known
from that smile on my face,

Was that five feet had just
crushed my best jump 'til that day.

It was two feet higher

than my mark in third grade,

When they started to track me

and how I behaved.

It was four feet higher than
in Middle school buzzing,

They said, "soon you'll be dead
or in jail like your cousins."

This mark was the highest
that had ever been set.

And after trying I knew
I was not quite done yet.

So, I stopped my odd dance
and wiped the grin off my face,

when I saw kids lining up
for some other great race.

But before I could make
for the next starting line,

I was boxed and closed in
by some old friends of mine.

Sent to track down

the fugitive child from Room 8,

for a quiet return to that class

to his place.

Once back there they tried
to downplay the whole scene,

Suggesting that life for me,
was just a pipe dream.

"There are round pegs
in your future,
these square holes must be filled,
it's good work for the hands
and your particular skills."

So, I sat there a while,
thinking maybe it's best
that they rescued and brought me
safe back to this desk.

Then I looked and took note, all the
names I could see,

Of the kids they had rescued
and returned before me.

There was Carla and Derrick,
John Tilson's name twice,

Rashida, Raymundo
and my long lost friend Mike.

So many more names
I did not recognize,

including one signed
A. Lincoln, class 1825.

And in the top right-hand corner,

between all of those lines,

There was just enough space

to finally make this seat mine.

But before eyes could dim back
to their early blank state,

I heard words again echoed
from the stands at that race.

Where my mother stood shouting,
and waving banners sky high,
"So what if you do fall down,
child? You most likely won't die."

Then a strange courage shook
and swept over me,

As I grabbed a hand full of
crayons and a big butcher sheet.

Starting a draft of the plans
I had long feared to speak,

I set goals for one hour,
one day, then one week.

And with those Popsicle sticks
I began to build up,

A small room when complete
was a full replica

Of this box where some said
I would live my life out,

Where none would see my lost face
or ever hear my mad shouts.

Then I placed on this model,

where brave lookers might see,

One red X on the wall

where that window must be.

Then glancing around
like I had not done before,

I spied keys to the locks
on a chain by the door.

And since all of the teachers

were busy passing crayons

and paste,

I left a note on their desk...

Gone to find

my next race ...

Hasan Davis began writing poetry at an early age with the encouragement of his mother, who he refers to as the international word wizard, Alice Lovelace, and his father, local Reggae Legend, Charles "Jikki" Riley.

"Following them across the city of Atlanta, I witnessed the birth of spoken word from two pioneers of the art. Initially, I think it was intended to occupy my time and energy, keep me out of trouble."

But there was no place that I would rather have been than in the front row mouthing along to their lyrical celebration of life, pain, and struggle like I was lip-syncing Stevie Wonder. This was how I learned to make sense of the chaos in the world I was navigating every day. Growing up experiencing ADHD and Dyslexia, I first created works with a natural cadence meant to be heard more than for reading.

Hasan's persistence paid off as he earned his GED. Then decided that college would be his next big step.

"This was a crossroads for me. I was still struggling, but I really wanted to make it. And for the first time I think I finally understood that the only person who could stop me from succeeding was me."

Today, Hasan has a bachelor's degree and a Juris Doctorate. He has served as Director of youth violence Prevention for the city of Lexington Kentucky and Commissioner of Juvenile Justice for the Commonwealth of Kentucky.

Hasan Davis is a Hope Dealer.

Hasan is committed to empowering young people and adults by assisting them in finding their voice, personal power, sense of self-respect, and dignity. He uses his passion for theater and the arts to ensure educators and leaders understand issues of equity and their role in ensuring all young people are engaged, encouraged, and empowered. He is internationally recognized as a speaker, educator, and advocate for youth.

"Each of us has a right to become the hero of our own story. Some of us just need more help finding the right cape ... and comfy boots!"

an imprint of Martin Sisters Publishing